A STAR SHONE

By Robbie Trent

Illustrated by Margaret Ayer

THE WESTMINSTER PRESS • PHILADELPHIA

THE BEAUTIFUL SECRET

In a little white house in the village of Nazareth, Mary was singing. And this was her song:

"I praise the Lord,
For he is good.
I love God's name."

Margaret Ayer

Over and over Mary kept singing the words. She sang them as she worked. She had been singing them ever since she heard the beautiful secret.

An angel brought the message to Mary. "God will send you a baby boy," the angel told Mary. "You must name the baby Jesus."

Mary hurried to Cousin Elizabeth's house in the hills. She was so happy she just had to tell someone. They were glad as they talked and worked together. And Mary sang again her thank-you song for the Baby Jesus who would come.

> "I praise the Lord,
>   For he is good.
>   I love God's name."

The angel had told Joseph the beautiful secret, too. "You and Mary must make a home for the Baby Jesus," the angel said. So when Mary came back from her visit, she and Joseph made a home in a little white house in Nazareth.

One day Mary and Joseph went on a trip to the little town of Bethlehem. The king had said they must go there to have their names written in his big book.

So Mary and Joseph started up the road to Bethlehem.

Over the hills and through the valleys they walked. The roads were full of people.

Bethlehem was full of people too. There were so many people that there was not room for Mary and Joseph in the inn. So Mary and Joseph went to a stable to sleep. And there, in the quiet nighttime, while the stars were shining, God sent Mary's baby boy.

Mary wrapped little Jesus in soft, white clothes. She made a bed of hay in a manger, and there she laid her baby.

In the fields outside the little town of Bethlehem, shepherds were watching their sheep, keeping them safe in the darkness. Suddenly the shepherds saw a shining light. They heard the voice of an angel of the Lord.

"Do not be afraid," the angel said. "I bring you glad news. The news is for all people. God has sent Baby Jesus to be your

Saviour and Friend. You will find him wrapped in swaddling clothes, lying in a manger in the little town of Bethlehem."

Then from the shining light there came the sound of voices of many angels singing a praise song to God:

"Glory to God
In the heavens above!
God sends his love
To all people."

The singing stopped. The angels went away. It was very quiet.

At last the shepherds spoke. "Let us go into Bethlehem,"

they said. "Let us go and see this baby of whom God has sent us good news."

One shepherd must have stayed to keep watch over the sheep. The others hurried into Bethlehem. They went to the stable of the inn. There they found Mary and Joseph. And there they found little Jesus, wrapped in swaddling clothes, lying in a manger.

When they had seen the baby, the shepherds hurried out to tell the glad news to everyone they met.

Inside the stable, Mary watched her baby as he lay sleeping on the hay. Very softly she sang her happy song to say thank you to God for little Jesus. And this was Mary's song:

> "I praise the Lord,
> For he is good.
> I love God's name."

Matthew, ch. 1; Luke, ch. 1 (parts)

Margaret Ayer

THE WISE MEN

It was long ago, in the days when Jesus was a baby. Far from the little town of Bethlehem there lived some men who studied the skies and watched the stars to see what they could learn from them. They were called wise men.

One night the wise men saw a bright star shining in the sky. "It is a new star," one wise man said. "Its light is brighter than any of the other stars."

"The King of God's people must be born," another wise man said. "Let us go to see him."

The wise men saddled their camels and started on their journey. They carried with them gifts for the new King— gifts of gold and frankincense and myrrh.

For days the wise men traveled over the sandy places. Pad,

pad, pad, went the camels' feet on the sand. Tinkle, tinkle, tinkle, went the silver bells that hung from the camels' necks.

On the wise men went, for days and days. Slowly, slowly, slowly, the camels climbed the high hills. Faster and faster, the camels trotted on the smooth places. And high on the backs of the camels rode the wise men, carrying gifts for the new King—gifts of gold and frankincense and myrrh.

At last the wise men came to the big city of Jerusalem. Pad, pad, pad, went the camels' feet on the streets of the city. Tinkle, tinkle, tinkle, went the silver bells that hung from the camels' necks.

The wise men stopped their camels and climbed down from their backs. They asked a question in King Herod's palace. "Where is the baby who is born to be King of God's people?" the wise men asked. "We have seen his shining star in the sky and have come to praise him."

14

But no one knew where the baby was. Even Herod did not know. He called his own wise men to come to help him. "Where is the baby who is born to be King of God's people?" Herod asked.

"He is to be born in the little town of Bethlehem," they answered, "for so it is written in God's Book:

> " 'From out the little town of Bethlehem
> Shall come the baby
> Who is to be King of God's people.' "

King Herod talked to the wise men about the shining star. "Go to Bethlehem," he told them. "Look carefully for this baby. When you have found him, come back and tell me."

Pad, pad, pad, went the camels' feet on the road to Bethlehem. Tinkle, tinkle, tinkle, went the silver bells that hung from the camels' necks. At last they came to Bethlehem. And

15

high in the sky, the wise men saw a bright star shining over a little flat-topped house.

The wise men stopped their camels and climbed down from their saddles. They went into the little house. And there they found the Baby Jesus with Mary, his mother.

The wise men knelt down. They opened their treasures and gave precious gifts to the Baby Jesus. The wise men gave gold, yellow as summer sunshine. They gave frankincense, fragrant with spices. They gave myrrh, soft and cool as the baby's cheek.

Then the wise men started back to their homes. Pad, pad, pad, went the camels' feet on the yellow sand. Tinkle, tinkle, tinkle, went the silver bells that hung from the camels' necks. But the wise men did not go by way of Jerusalem to tell King Herod where they had found the baby, for God sent them home by another way.

Matthew 2 :1-13

THE BABY IN THE TEMPLE

It was a happy day in the house where Mary and Joseph lived in Bethlehem. The Baby Jesus was almost six weeks old. It had been forty days since Mary had first wrapped her baby in soft clothes and laid him in a manger.

This morning Mary was up early. She rubbed little Jesus with smooth oil and wrapped him in a fresh swaddling cloth. She wound the clean linen bands about him from head to foot. Her baby was ready. Today she and Joseph would carry him to the beautiful Temple in the big city of Jerusalem.

Soon Mary was ready too. Her hair was shining and smooth, and her long dress was clean and white.

Joseph had been busy since before daylight. There was the donkey to water and feed and saddle. Then Joseph dressed in fresh clothes too. Now it was time to start.

Joseph led the donkey around to the door. He helped Mary up into the saddle and put little Jesus in her arms. Joseph reached for his long staff, and they started down the narrow street together.

Clippety, clop, clippety, clop, the donkey carried Mary and the Baby Jesus down the street and out to the road that led to the city of Jerusalem.

The baby snuggled close in his mother's arms. The donkey's pace was smooth, like the swinging of a cradle. The breeze sounded like soft music.

Clippety, clop, clippety, clop, the donkey carried Mary and little Jesus down the long road to the big city. Joseph walked by the donkey's side.

Mary held her baby close. Sometimes she sang to him. She sang again the song she had made to thank God when she first knew that he would send Jesus to be her little baby.

"I praise the Lord,
For he is good.
I love God's name."

At last the city was in sight. Joseph pointed to the shining roof of the Temple. He and Mary bought two pigeons to take to the Temple as love gifts. They left the donkey in a safe place and climbed the hill to the shining gate of the Temple.

Up the high, smooth steps, and through the gate, Mary carried the baby.

20

There she met an old man named Simeon, who had loved and served God for a long time. Simeon held out his hands to Mary and she put the Baby Jesus in his arms. Then Simeon bowed his head and prayed:

"Thank you, God;
Thank you for letting me see
The Baby Jesus."

Simeon turned to Mary. "Your child shall be great," he told her. "He shall help many people."

In the Temple there was an old woman whose name was Anna. She too had loved and served God for a long, long time. When Anna saw the Baby Jesus she thanked God for him. She told everyone the glad news of Mary's baby whom God had sent.

22

Mary and Joseph praised God too. They sang songs and gave the pigeons they had brought as gifts.

Then they started back home to Bethlehem.

Clippety, clop, clippety, clop, went the donkey's feet on the dusty road.

Mary held her baby close in her arms. She and Joseph sang together their song of thanks to God.

"We praise the Lord,
For he is good.
We love God's name."

Luke 2:22-39; Matthew 2:13-23

AS JESUS GREW

When Jesus was a baby, he lay sleeping almost all the time.
Sometimes he would cry, to tell his mother he was hungry.
Sometimes he would coo, and then she knew he was happy.
Sometimes he would smile as he curled his little fist around
Joseph's finger.

The Baby Jesus was growing. When he was six weeks old, he was big enough for Mary and Joseph to carry him to the Temple in Jerusalem. For a long time Jesus did not go back to the big Temple. He was too little, and he lived far away.

Every day the Baby Jesus grew. One day he could walk. Then before long he could talk. He could say, "Thank you," and, "Please."

And Jesus had birthdays—one, two, three, four, five, six of them. He could wash his hands and face. His mother could trust him to walk in safe places. He could say his prayers at night and in the morning.

Each year the Boy Jesus watched as Joseph and the neighbors got ready to go to the big Temple in Jerusalem. He listened as they sang the song of the Temple:

I was glad when they said to me,
"Let us go to the house of the Lord."

26

When he was all alone, Jesus played going to the Temple. And he sang:

> I was glad when they said to me,
> "Let us go to the house of the Lord."

"Someday when you are big, you too may go to the Temple in Jerusalem," Mary promised. "There you will hear the music of the silver horns and you will hear the stories of the people of God."

The Boy Jesus had more birthdays. He grew taller. He was seven, eight, nine, ten, eleven years old. He could take care of his clothes. He could carry water for Mary, and help Joseph in the carpenter shop. He knew many of the words and stories in God's Book.

Then Jesus had another birthday. He was twelve years old. "This year you may go with us to the Temple in Jerusalem," Joseph told him. Jesus helped Mary and Joseph get ready.

One day, they went singing over the hills with the neighbors, up the road to Jerusalem.

They walked, and walked. At last they could see the city. They could see the shining top of the Temple. The people began to sing. The Boy Jesus sang too:

> I was glad when they said to me,
> "Let us go to the house of the Lord."

Soon they were in the great city. In the Temple, Jesus listened as the teachers read from God's Book. He heard them tell stories from the Book. Jesus sat close to them, and asked

questions. The teachers would answer. Sometimes the teachers asked questions, and Jesus would answer.

At last the time came to go home. Mary went walking down the road with some neighbors. Joseph went walking down the road with some neighbors. It was not until night that they missed Jesus.

Straight back to the city Mary and Joseph went. And there they found the Boy Jesus talking with the teachers in the Temple. Jesus went down the road with Mary and Joseph, back home to Nazareth. But he remembered the beautiful Temple and all he had heard and seen there.

Every day Jesus learned more. Every year he grew taller. Every year he knew more about pleasing God and helping people. And every time he went to the Temple in Jerusalem, he sang the happy song:

> I was glad when they said to me,
> "Let us go to the house of the Lord."

Luke 2:40-52

29

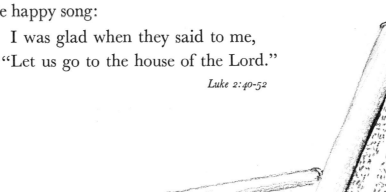

THE MAN WHO SAID "THANK YOU"

One, two, three, four, five—there were five sick men.
Six, seven, eight, nine, ten—there were ten sick men.

The ten men were sick. Their hands were sore. Their feet were sore. Their bodies were sore. They were lepers.

The sick men lived all alone outside a little town. They could not go to their homes, for their families might get sick too. They could not go to the next-door houses, for the neighbors might get sick too. They could not go to see their friends, for their friends might get sick.

No doctor knew how to make the ten sick men well. They must live all alone outside the little town.

"We wish we could go home," they often said to each other. "We wish we could go home to see our families. We wish we could go to see the neighbors. We wish we could see our friends inside the town."

One day the ten sick men heard news.

"There is a man who makes people well," someone told them. "His name is Jesus."

The sick men listened to the news. Then they looked sad and shook their heads.

"We could never find Jesus," they said. "We cannot go inside the town to hunt for him."

But one day the ten sick men were sitting by the side of the road. They heard footsteps on the road. They saw people coming. They heard many voices. "Jesus is coming!" someone shouted.

The sick men jumped to their feet. As loudly as they could, they called to Jesus.

"Please make us well," they begged.

Jesus looked straight at them. He knew how very much they wanted to go home to their families. He knew how much they wanted to go to see their neighbors. He knew how much they wanted to be with friends inside the town.

"Go into the town," Jesus told the ten sick men. "But go first to the Temple."

Right away they started running into the town. And as they ran, they found that their hands were not sore any more.

Their feet were not sore any more. Their bodies were not sore any more. The ten men were well.

One man stopped right where he was. He turned around and ran back to Jesus. He knelt down at Jesus' feet. He bowed his head. He said,

"Thank you, thank you,
Thank you, Jesus."

Jesus looked at the man who had been so sick. He looked far down the road and saw nine other men running into the town.

"Were not ten men made well?" Jesus asked.

Then Jesus smiled at the man who had come back to say, "Thank you." "Go home to your family and friends," Jesus told the man. "I am glad you are well."

The man went running into the town. As he hurried home his feet seemed to be sounding out the words:

"Thank you, thank you,
Thank you, Jesus."

Luke 17:11-19

JESUS AND THE CHILDREN

It was a sunny day in springtime. The road to the city was full of people. Men and women had left their work and their homes. Children had left their play. People had come from town and country, for they heard that Jesus was near.

The mothers had heard that Jesus was coming. They had washed the children's faces and combed their hair. They had helped them put on fresh, clean clothes.

Margaret Ayer

"We are going to see Jesus." This was what the mothers told their children.

"We are going to see Jesus," the children told each other.

Now the children and their mothers came walking down the road. There were big boys and girls, walking with long, long steps. They were on their way to see Jesus. There were little children too, skipping along with short steps. They were on their way to see Jesus. And there were babies in their mothers' arms. The babies could not walk even *one* step. But their mothers were carrying them to see Jesus.

"We want our children to see Jesus," the mothers told each other. "We want him to put his kind hands on our children's heads, and bless them."

Then far down the road they saw a crowd.

"There is Jesus," someone said. "All those people are listening to him."

The mothers and children went on down the road. Nearer and nearer they came to the crowd. The mothers pushed through the crowd until they were almost at the place where Jesus and his friends stood. Only a few more steps, and their children would see Jesus.

Suddenly they heard an angry voice.

"Be quiet," said one of the men near them. "Do not come here. Jesus is too busy to bother with children. You must not trouble him. Take your children away."

The mothers stopped. They turned away. The children stopped. They too turned away. Slowly, slowly, they started back through the crowd.

Then they heard another voice.

"Let the children come to me," Jesus was telling the men near him. "Do not send them away. In God's Kingdom there is room for all who love and trust as little children do."

The men said no more, but stood aside for the mothers and children to come nearer.

Straight to Jesus they came—the big boys and girls, the little children, and the mothers carrying their babies in their arms. How glad Jesus was to see each one!

He took the children in his arms and held them close.

He laid his hands on the children's heads, and blessed them, every one.

Then the children and their mothers went walking down the road again. The big boys and girls walked with long, long steps. They were glad, for they had been to see Jesus. The little children skipped happily along with short steps. They had been to see Jesus. And the babies smiled as they nestled close in their mothers' arms. They had been to see Jesus.

But what the children liked to remember best of all, was how glad Jesus had been to see *them*.

Mark 10:13-16; Luke 18:15-17; Matthew 19:13-15

ZACCHAEUS FINDS A FRIEND

Long ago, in the city of Jericho, there lived a very rich man. His name was Zacchaeus.

Zacchaeus had a big house to live in, and servants to do everything for him. He had good food to eat, and fine clothes to wear. He did not have to work very hard, and there was plenty of time to do as he pleased.

But Zacchaeus was lonesome. He had no friends to come to his big house and share his food. Men walked on the other side of the street, so that they would not have to meet Zacchaeus. No one wanted to have happy times with him when his work was done.

For Zacchaeus cheated people. He kept money that belonged to other people. He always took more than his share.

One day there was great news in the city of Jericho, where Zacchaeus lived.

"Jesus is coming!" Men and women talked about it in all the streets of the city.

"Jesus is coming!" The children ran home to tell their mothers. And all the people ran down the street to see Jesus.

Zacchaeus heard the news too. He ran down the street with the others. But Zacchaeus knew he could never see Jesus in that crowd, for he was a very little man. Even when he stretched up as tall as he could, Zacchaeus could not see over the heads of the people.

Now the street was full of people running. Zacchaeus was running too, for he had a plan. Straight to the big sycamore tree Zacchaeus ran. Up, up, the little man climbed to a high limb of the tree. There he sat, almost hidden by the leaves, watching for Jesus.

Soon Jesus came walking down the street. Zacchaeus could see the people crowding about him. Nearer and nearer they came to the tree where Zacchaeus was. Zacchaeus could see Jesus himself.

Now Jesus was under the tree. He stopped. Jesus looked straight up into the face of Zacchaeus.

"Zacchaeus," Jesus said, "come down from that tree. I am going home with you today."

The little man was so surprised that he almost tumbled off his seat on the high limb. Quickly he climbed down the tree.

The people stood aside as Zacchaeus walked proudly down the street with Jesus.

At his house Zacchaeus stopped and opened the door, and Jesus walked inside.

The people were watching. They frowned, and shook their heads. "Doesn't Jesus know that Zacchaeus has been doing wrong things?" they asked each other.

But Jesus was not thinking about what the people were saying. He was making friends with Zacchaeus, and talking with him. At last Zacchaeus had something important to tell Jesus.

"Jesus," Zacchaeus said, "I have done wrong, and I am sorry. I want to give half of all I have to the poor people who

need help. Many times I have taken more than my share. I will not do that any more. I will give back everything I have taken. I will even give back more. If I have taken one thing, I will give back four."

Jesus smiled. "Zacchaeus," he said, "I came here to be a friend to people like you. I came to help people love God and do the things that please him. What you have done this day is a happy thing."

Zacchaeus was glad. He knew he would never have to be lonesome any more. Jesus was his friend.

Luke 19:1-10